W

Up to

Worthiness

The Miraculous Journey of Inner Work

Melanie Weaver

Copyright @ 2022 Melanie Weaver

All rights reserved. No part of this book may be reproduced, copied, stored, or transmitted in any form or by any means—graphic, electronic, or mechanical, including photocopying—without the prior written permission of Melanie Weaver, except whereby permitted by law or in the case of brief quotations in critical articles or reviews with an accompanying credit that references the book title and author.

Book Title: *Waking Up to Worthiness:* The Miraculous Journey of Inner Work

Author/Publisher: Melanie Weaver
http://www.melanieweaver.online/; melaniemweaver40@gmail.com

Copyeditor: Heidi C. King,
River Editing: https://riverediting.weebly.com/,
EditorHeidiKing@gmail.com

ISBN Paperback: 979-8-9861354-0-3
ISBN eBook: 979-8-9861354-1-0

Published in the United States of America
Printed in the United States of America

*To the little girl and teenager inside of me
who passionately envisioned this book into being.*

CONTENTS

The complete transformation from 480 pounds to 170 pounds

PREFACE

By age 18, I was a single parent with a traumatic past. By age 26, I topped the scales at 480 pounds and could barely move without a cane. A year earlier, when I began the journey of writing this book, I was already well over 400 pounds and on welfare as a single parent of a five-year-old child. Although I was pursuing my degree in college to make a better life for myself and my son, I was still depending on my family for assistance. I felt so alone, ashamed, and hopeless at times. I felt like nobody understood me and that the task at hand was just too high of a mountain to climb.

At that time, 17 years ago, I wrote:

I hope to bring comfort and understanding to all those people that have been abused mentally, physically, sexually, or emotionally and have struggled with food addiction and obesity as a result. I wish to provide information to the public about obesity from an obese person's point of view. Society is handling obesity all wrong. There is so much judgement and so little empathy, compassion, and understanding because we, unfortunately, live in a society that is so externally focused and obsessed with physical appearance and unrealistic standards.

Everyone has problems and issues they suffer with in the human journey, but with obesity it's more physically visible.

In our society, it seems appearances and putting on a false persona of having it all together is much more valued than being real and authentic. We are all human beings who ought to be seen and treated equally. An effective and lasting solution to the obesity epidemic is not possible by approaching the problem with judgment, shaming, and cruelty. We need to come up with solutions that are based in compassion, empathy, understanding, unity, cooperation, and collaboration.

Have you noticed fat shaming is still generally accepted in the public and in the media? It's a very sad situation and in my opinion it's one of the biggest reasons people are getting more and more overweight and obese. I hope to inspire others that are currently feeling held back in their life because of their past histories, physical appearance, or self-esteem to find the resolve to believe in themselves again. There is absolutely good reason to have hope and to believe that you can still live a life you love and enjoy. You CAN become the person you were meant to be. I want to be a living example that any and every challenge in life can be turned into a valuable learning experience and victory.

I hope writing this book will help me to release the pain I have carried around for years and bring me even closer to becoming the person I want to be. I know deep within my heart and soul that all of you who struggle can accomplish this same task. Thank you, reader, in advance for the opportunity to share my story and journey of finding and reclaiming my true self by relinquishing the negative judgments, false beliefs, core wounding, and debilitating shame that I held within myself due to the life experiences that helped contribute to my obesity.

By believing in myself against all odds, I have now lost over 300 pounds, built an amazing career, and healed enough to be a great mother to my son, a leader to my co-workers, an effective healer, and a wonderful companion to my friends. The healing journey has brought me to a place where I now want to give back and inspire others to move forward in their lives to create whatever they desire.

I am not a doctor or counselor, so nothing offered here can be official guidance or advice, but hopefully my sharing will assist you somehow. For a very long time now I have lived this journey and walked this path of constantly investing in and transforming myself into better and better versions of me. No matter what your circumstance, you absolutely *can* improve your life and achieve the feelings of happiness, joy, and freedom you deserve! If I can move forward, so can you!

WE'VE GOT THIS!

ACKNOWLEDGMENTS

Writing and publishing this book has been a dream of mine since early childhood. There are many people in my life who inspired me to make the dream come true. At the top of the list is my son, Nicholas Weaver. Nick, you provided me with the experience of tangible unconditional love for the first known time in my life and the motivation to keep on keeping on in the darkest of times. Without you, I don't think I would have been able to make my dream a reality.

Next, I want to thank my beautiful mentor and best friend, Kerry Wekelo. Kerry, watching you masterfully and creatively approach each challenge that comes your way in life has inspired and driven me to new heights in my own life. I am forever grateful for your unwavering investment and belief in my abilities to achieve my dreams, even before you had any evidence that I could succeed. Thank you also for introducing me to my editor, Heidi King. Without you, Heidi, this book would not have captured my voice authentically and produced the level of quality I want to deliver into the world to help others who are struggling to make positive changes in their lives.

I also want to thank all of the incredible friends I have made over the years as well as my family members. Without all your love and support in overcoming the challenges and hurdles in my life, I would not have had the drive and determination to believe in myself and keep on climbing the mountains to get to the promised land of birthing my first book-baby!

And finally, I am so grateful to Source for fueling my Spirit with love, wisdom, and strength to keep following my heart's inner guidance.

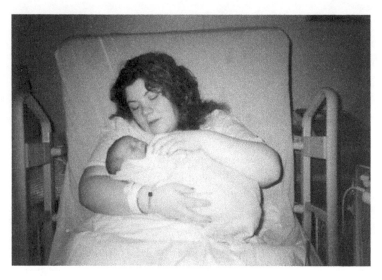

Me and Nick on Day 1 in 1999.

Acknowledgments

Me & Nick 10 years apart in 2010 & 2020

Celebrating my 40th birthday with my mom.

Celebrating the gift of soul level friendship with Kerry.

INTRODUCTION

Do you feel stuck in certain areas of life and struggle to move forward? Do you take one step and then feel insecurity and self-doubt creeping in and thwarting your progress?

For years, this kind of frustration plagued me and my efforts to make improvements in my life. With every failed attempt at self-improvement, my body grew larger, eventually trapping me in a prison of my own making. I spent many days buried in a deep, dark hole of doubt, trauma, desperation, and insecurity.

But then a miracle occurred. I learned that I could change anything I wanted in my life through introspection and inner work, and after fighting a losing battle against obesity for 36 years, I made 300 pounds disappear without exercise! I woke up to my own worthiness and discovered a deep place of love, healing, and acceptance that empowered me to find my true self and continuously improve my life.

I am so grateful for all that I have learned and all that I anticipate learning. Having made enough positive improvements in my life to keep the weight off for over two years now, I want to share some tips and information that may help you achieve your own goals and aspirations.

I am convinced there is no one-size-fits-all approach to weight loss and that sharing stories of success is one of the best ways to provide hope for positive change. Such personal stories also provide ideas and tools for strategies and techniques to try along the way.

And, as you will see in the details of my own healing journey, those tools are not limited to weight-loss attempts. They can be used to achieve success for any goal or aspiration you may have. So if you are facing challenges besides weight and health concerns, there's a good likelihood you will find some inspiration and wisdom in these pages to apply to those issues as well. If you are sick and tired of beating yourself up and feeling unsuccessful in your attempts to improve your life, this book is definitely for you. I know for certain that things can improve no matter the obstacles you may face.

In my personal journey, I have noticed that each accomplishment and achievement has caused me to love and value myself more, which has then resulted in me feeling new levels of worthiness along the way. I want to inspire you to also wake up to your own worthiness, to learn to truly love and accept yourself enough to allow into your life the dreams and wishes you have been longing for. My greatest hope is to uplift you and help you access the wisdom that will lead you to become your own best advocate. You absolutely can have fun while working toward becoming your best self!

Structure of this book

Chapter 1 begins with a summary of my overall journey toward healing and hope.

Chapter 2 delves into the details of my own inner work and discusses the infamous inner critic that we all must deal with if we want to make lasting changes or improvements in our life.

Chapter 3 gets into the nitty gritty details of my weight-loss journey and highlights the importance of investing in yourself.

Chapter 4 discusses shame spirals and how to navigate them as productively as possible.

Chapter 5 explores how to construct a realistic plan that will set you up for success in any endeavor.

Chapter 6 focuses on the importance of both discipline and flexibility as you implement a realistic plan.

Chapter 7 reviews ten keys to success that contributed to achieving goals in my own life that I didn't originally think were possible.

In **Chapter 8**, I share a few more stories of the additional miracles that have occurred in my life as a result of my continued commitment to inner work.

And in **Chapter** 9, I summarize the main points leading to inner and then outer healing and leave you with words of encouragement for the journey.

Whatever the reasons you are reading this book, I hope you will find something useful for your own life. May these pages

- inspire you and encourage you to believe in yourself no matter what your circumstances—to know that anything can be improved by making a sincere commitment to persevere and learn throughout your life journey;
- restore your hope if obesity and a battle with weight or food addiction has overwhelmed you to the point of losing hope;

- show you that the most effective and lasting self-improvement comes from self-acceptance, self-love, and self-compassion;
- convince you that you can absolutely make any changes and improvements you intend to make in your life; and
- motivate you to do the inner work and make your own dreams come true.

CHAPTER 1

HIGH MOUNTAINS

We are all a constant work in progress, and the journey is the most rewarding part.

My father had always wanted a daughter. His wish came true when I entered this world as baby Melanie. Just three years later, however, my little life turned upside down when my loving and doting father died in a car accident on his way home from work. His death devastated not only me but also our whole family.

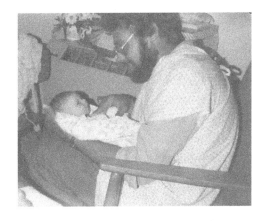

My first day of life with my dad.

I loved to listen to my daddy play guitar.

Feeling very much alone, I was forced to grow up quickly.[1] Adding to the trauma of my father's death, my family—like many families—handed down to me an overabundance of unhealthy belief systems, addictive behaviors, and undiagnosed mental illness from past generations. I had been given some very high mountains to climb. All of this contributed to me picking up many unhealthy behaviors and beliefs about myself that caused me to live a life of punishing myself because I thought I was bad.

Throughout my growing up years, I lived a double life because I felt inherently flawed and worthless. Yet, at the same time, I was always loving, curious, and intelligent. Luckily, I was

---

[1] My life story can also be found on my website at http://www.melanieweaver. online/.

able to make many lasting friendships along the way that helped me feel a sense of love and belonging outside my family life. Learning energized me and I excelled in school activities, but I made horrible choices that were a result of ingrained self-sabotaging habits from previous traumas. This led me to attract even more kinds of trauma, including abuse, overeating, rape, severely low self-esteem, and morbid obesity, to name a few. I did receive some therapy as a child, but my family did not allow me to continue treatment long enough to be of significant help; it threatened the status quo of our family life too much.

Around age six, I began to gain extra weight and morphed from being a fairly skinny child to what my family would describe as "chubby." From then on, my weight fluctuated constantly. Being overweight in my family was truly the worst thing, because most of my family members treated me like I had the plague. I remember so many insults and put-downs, with no one ever really trying to help me from a loving perspective. I felt so much anger and shame because it was clear that no matter how good of a person I was or how well I did in school, all that mattered, across the whole family, was that I was overweight. They told me on a regular basis how ashamed they were of me. In their minds, my excess weight reflected negatively on them.

It didn't take me long to begin dabbling in eating disorders, including anorexia, bulimia, and compulsive overeating. By middle school, I was able to let go of anorexic and bulimic behaviors, but compulsive overeating kept a strong hold on me. I was trapped by my eating behaviors and could not escape. I would lose and gain 60 pounds like it was nothing. Playing softball for several years helped me stay somewhat active despite being obese, but by the time I was 16 years old, I weighed 250 pounds. Then, during my senior year of school, I seesawed downward again, managing to descend to 185 pounds within a year by walking almost every day, restricting my diet intensely, and playing volleyball.

The up and down weight issues were not my biggest problem, however; underneath everything, my deepest issue was living with a lot of unresolved and unconscious trauma and not valuing myself. This led to many unhealthy and irresponsible choices throughout school. Luckily, my interest in my classes, awesome teachers, and amazing friendships were enough to keep me going. I managed to graduate from high school with honors and enrolled in college right away. Three months later, at age 17, I moved out of my mother's house and rented a place with my best friend.

Unfortunately, unresolved abuse and feelings of unworthiness made me an easy target for people to take advantage of me and manipulate me. I was also careless. Within several months, I found myself pregnant.

Immediately I withdrew from college. Most members of my family were massively ashamed of me and wanted me to get an abortion. Thankfully my mom stepped up and committed to help me make it work if I chose to keep the baby.

I had never planned to have kids, but this felt like destiny. Unlike many of my earlier life challenges, this was a mountain I *wanted* to climb! Deeply motivated to become a loving, effective, and quality mother to my child, I committed to making that happen no matter how hard the journey. I began reading self-help and parenting books to prepare for this new adventure.

A year after I graduated from high school, Nicholas was born. The journey to motherhood had been thrilling! My son's first moves inside the womb connected me to the cycle of life in such a deep way that I couldn't help but feel exhilarated. As each month passed, I fell more in love with the growing life inside of me.

Unfortunately, pregnancy did not love me back. The hormones and toxemia caused me to balloon up to 296 pounds at nine months pregnant and 250 pounds post-pregnancy. No matter what I did, I kept gaining weight.

Three years later, I finally started therapy again to find relief. Through the therapist's assistance and my own research, I learned that I had to consciously change the way I talked to myself. That was the start of a lifelong journey of reprogramming my inner dialogue and releasing beliefs that no longer served me. *Thank goodness I had been careless!* My son ended up being the motivation and inspiration I needed to learn to value myself enough to start healing.

A few times during Nicholas's first years of life I moved back home with my mom so I could be fully present for him. Four years after he was born, however, I decided I wanted to be able to support him without the help of my family. I wanted to give the two of us a fresh start together. So I headed back to college, even though I was so afraid I would not be able to fit in the classroom seats.

Fighting through my fears, I graduated with a two-year associates degree in business. As part of my coursework, I began an internship that ended up being the start of my now 17-year career in cybersecurity.[2] Right after graduation from college, I was able to move out on my own and luckily never had to return home.

After graduation, I was still gaining weight and my hormones were so messed up that my periods would sometimes last for two months. In a search for alternative healing methods, I came across the ancient healing art of Reiki. Reiki very effectively soothed my pain and increased my energy so that I didn't feel continually exhausted. The severity of my periods calmed down, and I gained a great sense of peace, which then allowed

---

[2] For seven of those years I served as a Project Manager and helped create a dream team experience that resulted in our team winning a prestigious Team of the Quarter award at the Coast Guard in 2015.

my mind to quiet down enough for me to more easily hear the still small voice inside of me.

While these improvements were wonderful, my hormones continued to fluctuate. By the second year after college, I ballooned up to 480 pounds. Suffering horrible knee and back pain, I knew if I did not pursue gastric bypass surgery I would not live long enough to be around to parent my son. So I underwent the surgery, and within two years I managed to drop down to 280 pounds.

Unfortunately, I was unable to lose any more weight until 11 years later. That's the point at which I finally decided I needed to be healthier and dove into learning about health, nutrition, and intermittent fasting. Through trial and error, I was able to lose another 110–20 pounds.

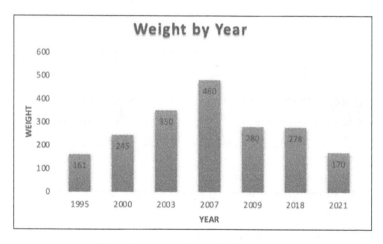

Chart depiction of weight fluctuations

I have maintained that weight loss for over two years now. Despite feeling extremely desperate and hopeless many times throughout my life, I kept getting up and trying again every day. I always believed that my intelligence, kindness, drive, and determination would take me far as long as I never gave up. And I had faith and knew there was a force within me that could help me accomplish much more than what the world told me I could achieve.

Over the years, that inner force led me to take many healing modality and spiritual growth classes. My own healing through Reiki, as well as my Reiki teacher's insistence and encouragement that I was a natural-born healer, inspired me to take three levels of training and become a Reiki Master. A few years later, I decided to study Sekhem, an ancient Egyptian healing system, for an entire year and became a master in that healing modality as well.

I also trained with my favorite international author over the course of two years to learn how to be an effective guide for others.

And over the past 13 years, I've studied Radiance Healing Light and many other classes offered by Spirit School for Intuitive Arts.[3] Through these courses I've met amazing mentors and healers who have helped me truly begin to value myself again and build myself back up.

And that's been the biggest lesson in all of this—learning how to love and value myself enough to invest in my own healing. I've had to re-wire my thinking, re-examine all my old limiting beliefs and programming, and be willing to dig deep into healing old wounds by learning how to treat myself the way I deserved to be treated.

Although this new way of being is still a great work in progress, I have reached a place in life that I never thought I would achieve. At this point, I will need multiple surgeries to remove excess skin, but once that happens I will have achieved my goal weight. Every single day I am amazed that after a lifelong battle

---

[3] See https://www.christenmccormack.com/spirit-school, founded by Christen McCormack.

with my weight, I am finally here, standing on top of a mountain with a beautiful view.

What I have known ever since I was a young girl has proved to be true: a person does not have to fit into society's standards to be successful. Perseverance and belief in myself has led to an incredible career, in spite of having only a two-year degree; an awesome parent-child experience and relationship that has taught me all about unconditional love; amazing friendships that have enriched my life in countless ways; a weight-loss journey where I dropped over 300 pounds without exercising;[4] spiritual and healing practices that have enhanced my everyday life; a loving relationship with a man I have known for 25 years; and leadership skills and abilities that have blessed many other people. Like my high school class motto borrowed from the Grateful Dead, what a long, strange trip it has been!

I am so grateful for and appreciative of the life journey I have traveled. Now it is my greatest hope to use all that I have learned and experienced to help others climb their own mountains to reach true peace, happiness, and joy.

---

[4] Now that I've lost enough weight that moving is more comfortable for me, I am adding exercise and it feels wonderful. I'm mostly walking and dancing, but I hope to add even more activities in the future. I encourage all of us to get as much movement as we can, but I remember how much it hurt when I was obese and had a bad knee. It would upset me so much how others never quite understood that it was not easy for me to "just eat less and move more"—like so many people who have never experienced obesity firsthand try to tell those of us who have been obese. If you have a hard time moving (like I did), you can still lose weight and achieve a healthier state.

Me making it to the top of an actual mountain hike

Enjoying the peace and serenity after the climb.

CHAPTER 2

THE INNER CRITIC

The most effective way to make any lasting change in life is to create a positive, supportive, and compassionate mindset.

OK. So, you are ready to make some changes in your life. Now what?

First things first. One of the greatest lessons I've learned in my 41 years of living is that the most effective way to make any lasting change in life is to create a positive, supportive, and compassionate mindset. Our attitude is a complete and total game changer when it comes to self-improvement. We must become our own advocate and practice patience, love, compassion, and understanding to our own selves the way we give it to others. If this is new to you, then it will require self-reflection, self-awareness, and a major mental shift in perspective. It certainly did for me.

One way to begin making the shift is to think of how you help and encourage the people you love in your life, and then begin helping and encouraging yourself in the same way. And if that doesn't work for you, imagine how you'd like others to treat you, and then treat yourself the same way.

It likely won't take long until you run into inner critics and judges. Aren't they so much fun to deal with as they ramble on and on about all the ways we aren't good enough, how everything we do is wrong, how awful we are, and how we will never amount to anything? Maybe your inner critic isn't as harsh as mine, but mine can be relentless. The key here is to first learn to get to know the voice inside of us that so freely expresses unhelpful and unsupportive opinions throughout our day, and then respond with more helpful, encouraging, and positive messages to ourselves.

To do this, we will need to take the time and make the space to notice what our inner critic is saying to us about the areas of our life we are attempting to improve or change. Once we can identity those thoughts, we can begin shifting them. This will lead, if we allow it, to us becoming our own biggest supporter, encourager, and motivator.

My own inner critic started wreaking havoc at a very young age. When I read back over my journals from age 16 and up, and many notebooks of poetry that I wrote at ages 13 and 14— wow, was I a mess! I was a wounded little girl with very low self-esteem who hated her body and herself because of her weight. For so long at those young ages, my self-esteem was like a puppet controlled by what I ate, how much I ate, what I didn't eat, and whether I exercised or not.

At 13 years of age, I wrote this poem, titled "Worthless":

I look at a mirror, but I see nothing.
Life is looking back at me and saying worthless.
I ask myself why, why is it so?
It is my own fault for being so weak.

So weak and so empty, so full of nothing.
I sit and I think but no action occurs.
Expecting it to come to me as if it were a gift.
As if I don't even have to go and get it.
BUT that isn't so, action is required.
So why won't I seek what I wish for?
Where is my willpower when I need it most?
It has disappeared and all I can do is hope it will reappear
When it does, I will be here—
Ready to take on the term worthless.

So many passages in my writing overflowed with "I hate" statements for every part of my body. I think the only things I liked about myself were my eyes and my ankles. Later in life when I become morbidly obese, my ankles would swell up terribly, so then I didn't like even them very much. Can anyone relate? I have a feeling many of you can, especially if you are female.

The journal excerpts below, when I was 14–16 years old, exemplify the crazy cycles I put myself through while trying to lose weight, including one fast that lasted for 18 days. I believe these attempts to address only the physical aspects of the issue set me up to keep gaining weight and to eventually peak at more than 480 pounds. At the beginning of these journal entries, I had drawn a very obese, round person with tears flowing. I wonder if any of you can relate to this way of thinking below:

14 Years Old

January 12

Tomorrow I pray is the day I really begin to get serious about losing weight. When I get hungry, I need to write my feelings down. Why can't I seem to get control of myself and my eating? I've got to lose weight again and be thin. I'm ready to change and be a happy person. It makes me so disgusted to look in the mirror. I feel like such a failure and a disappointment to everyone around me. I want to feel

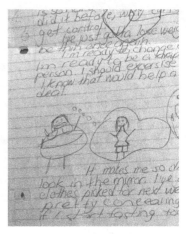

Me drawing my visualizing into a picture.

wanted again. I have my clothes picked out for next week and they are fairly concealing. I figure if I start fasting tomorrow, I will drop 10–15 pounds by next Monday. I really hope I can follow through this time.

January 13

Well again I failed and screwed up. I went to Red Lobster and ate all kinds of food. I am so irritated with myself. I guess I am just a complete and utter failure. I don't know when I will stick with this and actually go through with it, but I hope it's soon. I just don't understand why I can't go through with it. Tomorrow I have to not eat! No question about it! I just hope I really do it this time."

15 Years Old

January 22

Guess what! I didn't eat anything today! Last night I did Abs of Steel and I walked back and forth from Mammaw's house today. I'm so proud of myself. Tomorrow I am going to start eating healthy and keep record of what I eat. My plan soon is to get a discman and walk to school for exercise.

March 8

Well my life as far as dieting goes has been totally off the wall and a rollercoaster. In the last 15 days, not counting today, I fasted 9 days and ate for 6 days. I've went through about 3 hunger attacks and have vomited on about 3 of the days I have eaten. I hate vomiting. I am so hungry right now, but I can't eat. I know I can't. It's so hard. This Lint [Lent] thing for church is supposed to be when you give up something or fast. I wanted to fast for 40 days, but it didn't work.

I am going to try and keep going. I need to beat my record of not eating for 18 days in a row. I am going to do this the right way this time with drinking lots of water, V8, and fruit juices. I was walking for a while, but the weather has been way too cold. Today will be the 5th day I haven't eaten. I did get my discman. I went to the doctor's office on February 9th and I weighed 220. I could not believe it! I weigh 195 now, so that is 25 pounds on my 1st month of being serious. That's good and I did that with only following the plan for half the month. If I could just keep going, then I would be down to 180 by April, 160 by May, and 140 by June. I know I can do this. There is a power in me that wants this for me! I hope Mother Nature pitches in and gives me some good weather!

16 Years Old

February 23

Well it's been almost a year. I continue to fail and weigh about 232 right now. I'm big, ugly, and disgusting. I am going to try and do well tomorrow. I am going to try and take it day by day. I'm just so unhappy and feel so stuck. If only I would have stuck with it before, things would have been okay.

July 12

I'm still doing great. I weigh 192.5 now! That is a total of 53.5 pounds. I look a whole lot better, but I still have 62 pounds to lose to reach my goal of 130 pounds. I joined the local gym 3 weeks ago. I did go off my diet for a whole week recently. I was super disappointed, but I got back on my plan. I found some pictures of myself from February, and I look so terrible. I can't believe how fat I was and still am. I feel extremely gross. I know I am doing everything I can right now and hopefully by Christmas I will look excellent. I walked over 2 miles today, went to the gym, only had 610 calories, and drank 8 glasses of water. I feel okay.

July 14

Today was great. I walked 5 miles, worked out for an hour, painted a fence, and raked a hill for an hour. I only ate 500 calories and drank 8 glasses of water. I get weighed tomorrow.

Even though I had recorded my self-sabotaging in plain sight, I couldn't see it until I was about 22 years old. At that point, I weighed well over 400 pounds, had moved back in with my family so I could be a good mom and take care of my son, and my anxiety and depression were so out of control I felt like I was going to die unless I went inside myself to find answers. And dying was not a viable option, because I wanted to live for my son; he was *the only reason* I wanted to live.

Life was so difficult for me, and my weight just kept rising. My body hurt, and I had to get in and out of the grocery store in ten minutes or less because my knees would be aching and the sweat would be dripping off of me. My body stank, and I was so embarrassed to be seen. I was heartbroken from all the "love relationships" that never seemed to work out because I was not good enough or too fat. And I felt like I was failing my son as a parent because I could not move around very well and physically play with him like he deserved. I overcompensated in other ways and also made sure he had such outlets with (thankfully) my family—mom, grandparents, aunt, and uncle.

Then there was the daily disappointment and disapproval from my family that weighed me down even more. Being fat was like the plague to them. In their eyes, I was a person with a horrible, disgusting, shameful, self-inflicted disease. Because some of them didn't know how to deal with my obesity and felt helpless to change it, they would throw insults at me, telling me I was repulsive, gross, huge, embarrassing.

What did I do about all of this? I believed them and ate more food! I used my fat to protect me from being hurt. It didn't work. But I did not realize what I was doing until many years later.

Instead, I lost it mentally and emotionally. I had a major breakdown and decided it was time to get help and go to therapy. My entry-level customer service job at the time provided short-term disability, which allowed me to work with doctors and a therapist to see what I could do to change my life. I wanted to lose weight. I wanted to go back to college. I wanted to be the mom my son deserved. I wanted to feel good about myself. I wanted to be healthy. And I wanted to stop needing other people to help me, so I could move away from their negativity, unkindness, and dysfunction.

That's when I began researching. I read books and attended therapy and found all kinds of information about how our brain works and how our thoughts have everything to do with the life we live. I found many books and programs that centered around changing my thoughts and the way I talked to myself. This was revolutionary to me! I had faith, but I did not realize I had the power to change my thoughts. I had seen the concept before, but I just had not understood it.

Little by little I became more aware of what was going on inside of me, especially in my mind. Although I began to feel a bit better, I was unable to let go of all the self-hatred that had built up inside of me from years of wounds created by all the shame I felt. It was not going to be an overnight job, for sure.

I stuck with it though, even when I was not seeing any results. I began recognizing and writing down what I was thinking and saying to myself—specifically, all the critical thoughts that never seemed to take a break. Once I started this practice, something led me to write down positive thoughts to replace the critical ones and then to start saying these new thoughts inside myself in response to each negative thought. For a few months, I diligently carried a notebook around and documented my thoughts. This was hugely helpful and a crucial beginning for me to start believing I could make positive changes in my life.

I learned how greatly we are all impacted by our upbringing, including the culture we were raised in. As we grew up, what we saw, the messages we heard, and all the societal standards drilled into us by advertisements created an inner critic in us that confirmed we weren't good enough and didn't measure up. As adults, we take over the role of this inner critic and start repeating the negative messages to ourselves.

On another note, I had also relied heavily on my faith and spirituality as an immovable rock in my life. I knew that even if no one else loved me, a power somewhere inside or outside of me did love me and did want good for me.[5]

For me, like many addicts—and I was quite the food addict—I needed something more powerful than myself to rely on. After all these years, I have finally developed a strong and loving relationship with myself and have become the savior in my own life that I was always needing. My spirituality still guides my life, and it is what has provided me with the inner power, strength, and wisdom needed to lose 300 pounds and keep it off, among many other accomplishments in life.

In my search to dissect, understand, and improve my relationship with food, I joined Overeaters Anonymous and read several weight-loss books. In some of the books, I was introduced to the idea of affirmations, which seemed silly to me at the time. The suggestion reminded me of those crazy Saturday Night Live skits from when I was a kid, where someone would stand in front of a mirror saying nice things to themselves. But I was desperate and willing to try anything.

So, I started saying affirmations to myself. Some of the most powerful ones were *I love myself* and *I trust myself*. The one that helped the most was *I accept myself*.

I soon realized that saying the affirmations was not much different from writing down my thoughts and creating new, more positive ones. Either way, I started feeling better, even though I was then around 400 pounds, could not fit into a booth at a restaurant or squeeze into a movie theater seat (for seven years!), and had a hard time bathing and walking.

---

[5] I am describing my personal journey here. I don't know what belief system is right for anyone else. We are all on our own journey, and I respect all paths.

I also stopped defining myself by outside standards. At the same time, I began noticing and documenting all the things I was good at and characteristics that I did like about myself. Eventually I began feeling confident enough to go back to college and begin working toward providing a good life for my son.

One of the next pivotal actions steps I took was to get real about all the reasons I wanted to lose weight, get healthy, and feel better. Identifying and documenting this information motivated me to keep going when things got especially hard or when I messed up. I made the following list when I was 23 years old:

Reasons I Want to Lose Weight

- *I want to feel better.*
- *I want my back and knees to stop hurting.*
- *I want to be able to play with Nick more.*
- *I don't want to get short of breath anymore.*
- *I don't want to be so tired and so achy so much of the time.*
- *I don't want to feel so gross and have my fat touch everywhere on my body.*
- *I want to move faster and not have to sit for so long.*
- *I want to feel better about myself and be healthier.*
- *I want to feel comfortable going more places and not be so insecure around people.*
- *I want to fit in booths at restaurants and normal sized chairs in other places.*
- *I don't want to be so self-conscious and have to feel other people's harsh judgement.*
- *I want my family to stop giving me a hard time.*
- *I don't want Nicholas to have a fat mommy.*
- *I don't want the people who care about me to worry about me dying.*

- *I want to fulfill the purpose in my life and do more for Spirit, as well as help others.*
- *I want to have normal loving relationships.*
- *I want to be able to get better jobs and not be discriminated against.*
- *I don't want people to give me weird looks.*
- *I don't want my body to sweat and smell bad so easily.*
- *I don't want to have so many limitations.*
- *I want to be able to put shoes and socks on like normal.*
- *I want to fit into cars normally and be able to walk more.*
- *I want to walk more and be able to go to an amusement park and fun places.*
- *I don't want to die of obesity. I want to have a normal life span.*
- *I don't want to die and then have to be lifted out of the house with a crane.*
- *I want to be able to finally look in a mirror and say, "You look ok or good."*

At that time, I lost 20–30 pounds by trying all kinds of different diets, including Weight Watchers, Atkins, South Beach, and Vegetarianism. But nothing worked long term. My hormones were totally out of whack, and I consistently gained all the weight back.

In spite of the yo-yo dieting, however, I continued to press forward. I attribute that perseverance to all the new, positive messages and encouragement I was giving myself, combined with my faith that there was a guiding force that wanted good for me.

Five months after I began the practice of affirmations, I decided to write out all the things I would accomplish with the help of my spirituality and inner guidance system:

1. *I expect and believe that Spirit will deliver me from my food addiction and give me everything I need to lose weight starting right now.*
2. *I will be delivered from smoking and all unharmful substances.*
3. *I will overcome the spirit of laziness and be given energy to accomplish all that I need to do in my life.*
4. *I will learn how to love myself.*
5. *I will learn how to control my thoughts.*
6. *I will develop and use self-control and discipline.*
7. *Good opportunities will constantly come my way.*
8. *I will do well in college and obtain my Associates Degree.*
9. *Spirit will bring me a great job.*
10. *I will fulfill the purpose of my life and live the life that I was meant to live helping others.*
11. *I will continuously be provided with the insight, knowledge, wisdom, strength, perseverance, and love I need to progress on my journey of self-improvement.*

Many of the items on the list came true quickly. For instance, I managed to graduate from college, and at 25 years old I landed an awesome job that allowed me to completely move away from my family and fully support my son by the time I was 26. Luckily, I have never had to go back to depending on my family, and I was able to provide my son with a good life. He is 22 now and looks back on his childhood very fondly.

For other items on my list, I didn't see progress until many years later. And some goals I'm still working on, like living my purpose.

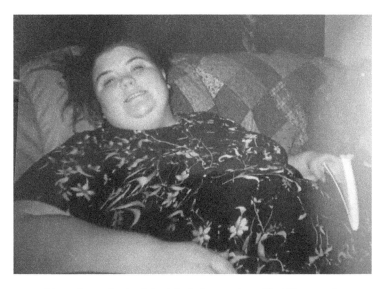

Me trying to be joyful while being a miserable 480 pounds

Doing my best to provide Nick a happy Christmas.

License Pic at my biggest.

I remember feeling like I was trapped inside my body.

One goal that consistently eluded me, no matter what I tried, was losing weight and beating my food addiction. Even an attempt to schedule weight-loss surgery several years earlier had failed when insurance denied coverage for the procedure. After seven years of horrible periods, my body hurting every single day, and going to extremes—fasting for days at a time, starving myself, attempting to make myself throw up, and trying all the fad diets—I felt at a total loss. For me, food was love and I couldn't give it up.

Then one day I fell in the parking lot at work. It was mortifying! Plenty of people could see me from the three-story office building, and it wasn't a simple matter for me to get back up. I had hurt my knee badly and had to maneuver my body a great deal to manage to stand back up. There I was, 26 years old with a six-year-old child, trying to figure out how to support 480 pounds despite unbearable pain from a torn meniscus.

Following doctor's orders, I ended up buying a cane, began receiving regular cortisone shots in my knee, and started taking a steady prescription of pain killers and antidepressants just to deal with day-to-day life. The way people looked at me during that time was brutal. I could feel their judgment, and it hurt me so much.

I knew that if something did not change quickly, my weight was going to kill me, and my son was going to lose his only parent. That thought absolutely terrified me, so I surrendered and decided for the second time to pursue gastric bypass surgery.

In order to qualify for the procedure through my work insurance, I had to first comply with a series of tests, evaluations, and procedures. They had to determine if the operation was medically necessary and if I was emotionally and physically stable enough to withstand the process. Miraculously, the answer came back yes.

But there were more hurdles to jump. The initial yes didn't mean I could proceed. The surgeon would not operate on me until I proved I could lose 5–10 percent of my body weight to ensure that I could successfully withstand such a huge rearrangement of my digestive tract. My body turned out to be so resistant to weight loss that the doctor postponed the surgery a month or more. Only after I went on a completely liquid diet could I lose the 30–40 pounds required for the procedure.

Unfortunately, a high percentage of people regain a significant amount of weight within 10–12 years of gastric bypass surgery.[6] My personal belief is that this is often the case because people don't take the needed time to go within themselves and understand why they began overeating in the first place and what payoffs they received for being overweight.

Such lack of inner exploration is easy to understand; changing our patterns and behaviors is a huge commitment. It's no easy thing to break an addiction, and food addiction is especially challenging because a person can't totally eliminate food from their daily life. This means you must be willing to completely change your relationship with food and your body. In my case, I was so in my head and so disconnected from my body for such a long time that my physical self felt separate from me. Not until the past few years did I truly begin tuning in to my body and make the decision to love and care for it.

Thankfully, the bariatric surgery was successful, and I lost somewhere between 180 and 200 pounds in the first 18 months after surgery. After regaining some weight, I ended up somewhere around 280 pounds and stayed there for about 10 years. I never managed to drop under 260 pounds or so until the past three years.

---

[6] See, for example, Mayo Clinic, "Weight Regain after Bariatric Surgery," June 13, 2018, https://www.mayoclinic.org/medical-professionals/endocrinology/news/weight-regain-after-bariatric-surgery/mac-20431467; and Daniela Vicinansa Monaco-Ferreira1 and Vânia Aparecida Leandro-Merhi, "Weight Regain 10 Years after Roux-en-Y Gastric Bypass," *Obesity Surgery* 27 (October 31, 2016): 1137–44, https://doi.org/10.1007/s11695-016-2426-3.

Enjoying an amusement park for the first time in 7 years.

Me at work 1 year post surgery.

30th birthday – 2 years post-surgery.

During those 10 years, I looked a lot better, felt a lot better, and my health improved, but I was still obese and did not experience the initial success many weight-loss surgery patients do. I assumed it was because of how much I had weighed going into the surgery. I hoped that one day I would be able to lose more weight and deal with the extra skin on my body, but a big part of me did not believe it would happen. Nevertheless, I continued to work on becoming my best self.

During my thirtieth year, I buckled down and became very serious about seeking deeper internal healing. I knew I was still holding on to some pain from the past, so I set out to begin forgiveness work.

I began by taking the time to identify all the situations in my life where I still felt hurt, betrayed, or in pain. I looked at my resentments and made lists of all the people I was still feeling unresolved issues with from my past. In the process, I learned that the greatest task at hand was to forgive myself for using fat as protection from all that had happened to me. As I faced the fact that I had trapped myself in a 480-pound prison of my own making, I focused on a new affirmation: *I now manifest complete love and acceptance of myself. I feel secure, confident, happy, peaceful, and joyful.* Then I wrote the following letter to myself. I believe it created a pivotal beginning to my later success:

Dearest Melanie,

You have grown and evolved so much throughout this lifetime. I am so proud of you, and I fully forgive you for all the mistakes or actions that you made that were not in your own best interest. I now release all the shame and self-defeating statements and behaviors from the past. I forgive you for becoming addicted to food and other self-sabotaging behaviors you used to try to fill the voids you felt inside. I forgive you for abusing yourself and your body. I forgive you for allowing other people to use, manipulate, and take advantage of you. I forgive you for being so vulnerable in love relationships and allowing men to treat you in ways that did not value your worth. I forgive you mostly for not loving yourself as much as you have deserved and for accepting way less than you deserve because of that. You are beautiful just the way you are and are Spirit's magnificent creation. I love you so much. I accept you as you are. You have so many good things to look forward to in the future. You will feel happy and loved and achieve your heart's desires one day.

Now fast forward seven years to my decision that it was time to see if more could be done to successfully lose weight. I was ready and willing to make a huge commitment and investment in my health because I believed my body and I deserved it. Also, at that point my son was 18, which meant I could shift the focus of my life back to me and making improvements in my own life.

I didn't know if I could lose any more weight, but I had learned to love and accept myself exactly how I was, so I decided I ought to give it another sincere effort. I felt so much gratitude that I had lost and kept off enough weight from the gastric bypass that I could go to the movies, fit in booths at restaurants, walk and stand more than 10 minutes at a time without my body aching, and perform normal day-to-day tasks like bathing and dressing without discomfort or pain. And I was so grateful I could do fun things with my son and provide him the life and mother he deserved to have.

I had been given a second chance at life, which made me appreciate everything in a much deeper way than I had before. I finally felt worthy enough of losing more weight so that my body could feel and look even better. Excited about life, I became hopeful that I could find even deeper happiness and fulfillment.

In my journey toward self-love, self-acceptance, and self-worth, change came slowly and required patience, compassion, and mindfulness. Little by little, as I allowed good things into my life and succeeded in a variety of endeavors, I realized I could do more and that I also wanted and deserved more. I began thinking about setting boundaries in my life, and this led me to the life-changing decision that I was not going to accept people or situations into my life where I would be treated with less care and respect than I deserved.

These efforts led to positive growth in my work as well. Over the course of three years, I became a leader by slowly climbing the career ladder from security analyst to team lead and then to project manager three years after that. In that role, I invested in each of the 17 people I oversaw on my team; I learned what drove them, what they were talented in, what was important to them, and—at the top of the list—what they enjoyed doing.

Being that kind of leader helped me determine what my team needed from me to in order to bring the very best out in them and what tasks would be most well suited for them. Through my leadership experiences, I learned that we are all motivated and inspired by different things and that one of the greatest keys to success of any kind is for people to determine for themselves what their specific motivators are. These methods were highly successful in creating a productive, thriving, and enjoyable work environment.

Seeing this heartfelt experiment be so successful in the information technology (IT) field got me thinking about how these methods might apply to my personal life and goals. I began asking myself the same questions I had asked of my team members: *What drives me? What are my greatest talents? What is important to me? What brings me joy?* That whole experience was an aha moment that showed me I needed to invest in myself as much as I invested in other people. It helped me get to the point where

I could succeed in taking my own health more seriously and, eventually, in achieving my lifelong goal of losing weight and keeping it off.

The time had come, I realized, for me to become the leader in my own life, where things were not going so well. My grandparents, who were more like my parents and very close to my son, had both died very sad deaths—first my grandmother and then my grandfather two years later. This caused my whole family to part and go separate ways. My son, triggered by the emotional upset of losing his greatest role model and father figure in my grandfather, developed Crohn's disease at age 14. About two years later, during a time when I was needing to do the job of three people at work, he ended up having 18 inches of his bowel removed. To make matters worse, my marriage was crumbling. All of this sent me even deeper into financial debt than I had already sunk from the challenges of being a single parent.

By the end of that year, all the drama and trauma had worn me down and drained me dry. I was scraping the bottom of my emotional barrel and desperately needed a change. A BIG change.

CHAPTER 3

OPERATION MELANIE

It's time to choose you.

Up to this point, I had put everything and everyone ahead of myself, and I was tired of living as though I didn't exist. As if none of my needs and desires mattered. It was time to choose Melanie and reclaim my life!

So I made the firm decision to give myself a total reset. I had relied on food and wine to numb the pain of overwhelming stress, and my health was not good. I needed to experience some personal success and to believe in myself again. I needed a boost to prove to myself that I had the strength to create a better life.

When I was 37 years old, I wrote the following in December:

Now is the time for me to get motivated for myself to become everything I want to be and experience, such as: confident, sexy, secure, self-assured, beautiful, creative, talented, intelligent, and competent. I want to be connected to my Spirit and get clear and accurate guidance and information to help myself and hopefully others in the future.

After making sure my son was back on track with his health and treatment plan, I set out to make severe changes. I asked my husband to move out and filed for a divorce. Then I left the job I loved after having worked there more than 10 years. The following month, as I was contemplating next steps, I felt a call to create and embody more confidence, self-love, and self-acceptance. That idea led me to turn to my health so I could feel good.

I began by drinking less wine. Then I shifted into wanting to eat better. That same month I decided to enact "Operation Make Melanie Optimal and Enlightened." I spent all of the next month saying affirmations, documenting my goals, visualizing what I wanted, praying for help and support, listening to inspiring audio books, and making preliminary plans to prepare myself for the task at hand.

Operation Melanie included the following affirmation statements and thoughts:[7]

This is the year I choose myself and nurture me instead of caretaking everyone else. I will feel peace and joy. I have calmness. I feel good about myself. I enjoy my work again. I am confident. I forgive myself for everything. I love and accept myself as I am. I only participate in relationships with others who are self-sufficient, loving, kind, and giving. I am connected to my Spirit and live my purpose. I feel good, joyful, confident, secure, and comfortable in my own skin. My life is joyful and fun and is full of adventure, laughter, wonderful experiences, and people. I am filled with my own beauty and light and bring inspiration, joy, and love everywhere I go. Every area of my life is uplifted as I embody the energy of confidence, security, and joy within myself everywhere I go. I am falling in love with myself. I am getting myself back. I am healing. I love life and

---

[7] I wrote these statements four years ago, on January 1, 2018.

life loves me. I feel confident, sexy, worthy, beautiful, radiant, and capable of all things. I decide to only accept what is good for me and what feeds, loves, and supports my Spirit. I embody confidence, self-acceptance, self-love, and self-empowerment.

At 278 pounds, I wanted to see weight-loss results quickly. So when my massage therapist told me about one of her clients who had successfully lost weight using hCG (Human Chorionic Gonadotropin) injections, I signed up without hesitation. The medically supervised program I entered cost $1,200, lasted 12 weeks total (including six weeks of self-maintenance), required following a strict protocol of eating fewer than 500 calories a day, and included taking hCG injections for 40 days to curb hunger. The program was very restrictive and extreme, but it absolutely worked to give me the initial boost of weight loss I was seeking.

Every week I would go in to talk to the doctor and weigh in. Six weeks into the program, by the end of April, I had lost 44 pounds and weighed 234. By the end of May, I weighed in at 230 pounds. I was so happy and proud of myself for sticking with it, but I knew there was no way I could maintain that kind of restrictive program long term. I missed the variety in my diet. It was time for a new technique to lose weight.

So I decided to try a ketogenic diet.[8] After a few months of that, I added intermittent fasting. My friend from work had sent me information on this type of fasting, and I realized very quickly that there was a great deal of science behind it. I found multiple sources of research and literature to support its benefits. I had fasted some when I was young and had enjoyed the mental clarity it gave me, so I was open to trying it again. This time I ate only during an eight-hour window—between 12 p.m. and 8 p.m.

_____

[8] The keto diet I followed allowed only 20 grams of carbohydrates per day.

each day. During the fasting hours, I could drink water, tea, and black coffee (no cream or sugar) to hold me over.

Fasting made sense to me, and it's now probably my favorite weight-loss strategy. I am still using it today and plan to fast regularly for the rest of my life because my body truly enjoys the way it feels during intermittent fasting and other forms of fasting. Six months after the hCG injections, I was able to get down to 225 pounds. Then life happened, and I crept back up to 242 by the end of the following month—a gain of 17 pounds.

Looking ahead to the following three months—October through December—I made a list of goals to help me get back on track. Although I did not successfully meet all of those goals, having the list helped me hold myself accountable.

1. *I track my food in* Fitness Pal *every day.*
2. *I abstain from drinking alcohol.*
3. *I meditate at least 5 minutes a day.*
4. *I exercise using the* Sweating to the Oldies *DVD.*
5. *I eliminate sugar from my diet. I eat healthy.*
6. *I spend time alone writing and mapping out my book.*
7. *I work on my website.*
8. *I lose weight and get back on track to where I was.*

And I did not let this setback deter me. Instead, I picked myself right back up and began following a keto diet and intermittent fasting again and got down to 202 pounds in March of the following year. This gave me a total weight loss at that point of 76 pounds in one year. I was so excited and proud of myself! At 202 pounds, I was so close to sliding under the 200-pound mark. I had thought I would *never* would see a number lower than 200 on the scales. In a typical week, I lost 1–3 pounds, and for the year I lost an average of 1.4 pounds a week. For 9.5 of the 12 months that year, I ate a healthy diet and stuck to a plan. For the other 2.5 months, I fell completely off plan.

At the end of March, I finally did it; I dropped down to 199 pounds! Amazed and grateful, I felt as though I had reached the highest peak of Mt. Everest! I was so happy. That was such a monumental moment for me. I had not weighed that "little" for 20 years—since I was 18 years old. The following month, I fell off the wagon and rose back up to 213 pounds after a few weeks of unhealthy choices. Luckily, once again I picked myself right back up and returned to my healthy eating plan. By the end of May, I had managed to dip down to 193 pounds.

I learned so much in that year, and, for the first time, I began to actually like healthier food. I also did not judge myself or beat myself up when I fell off my healthy eating plan. I realized it was part of being human and that it was OK.

Life is all about choices and consequences. It's about knowing how your body will react to different foods. Moderation and balance are truly the way to go. I proved to myself that if I wanted to achieve and maintain weight loss and feeling healthy, I must have more days making healthier choices than making unhealthier ones. It was never too late, and I could start over at any time. It was ok to treat myself. Deprivation is not ever the answer! Making a commitment to love and respect my body was the most important decision and key success factor of this whole operation.

Around the 11- to 12-month mark, when I had lost 54 pounds or so (before I dropped under 200 pounds), I dove into much more research about fasting. My findings led me to try a five-day Fast Mimicking Diet called ProLon, based on the Longevity Diet, that I had heard about at the doctor's office when doing the hCG protocol. I wanted to reset my body and challenge myself.

After I successfully completed that program, my body started craving healthy foods like avocados, olives, eggs, almonds, cucumbers, broccoli, tomatoes, and lemon water. I was *amazed* as this had never happened to me before! My body actually shifted what it wanted, and I was now able to understand and read its communication cues more accurately. This was truly an extraordinary miracle for me, and since that point more than two years ago I have continued to crave healthy food. I still crave unhealthy food sometimes as well, but my body lets me know when it's not happy with my food choices by causing me digestive issues.

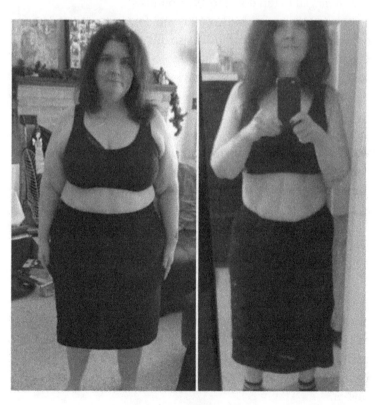

Front View of Progress.

Side View of Progress.

Before this point, I had always craved only junk food. I found it incredible that when I learned how the body works and gave it high-quality fuel and nutrition, my body returned the favor by rearranging cravings to make it easier to stay on track with making healthy eating choices.

One of several helpful online resources I discovered was Dr. Mindy Pelz's YouTube channel. I learned through her and other sources that our body is like a luxury vehicle with all the bells and whistles; the problem is that we were not taught how the features work and how to utilize them. What a cool concept! I also learned from Dr. Pelz that it's not necessarily a positive thing for women to eat low-carb all the time, because this can negatively affect our hormonal balance. I learned that planning a feast day each week to eat healthy carbs and treat myself was an effective way to be successful.

I have never believed that there is a one-size-fits-all approach to losing weight and becoming healthy. Instead, I've always hoped for and planned to find a balance in my life somewhere in the middle between the extremes. So I continued to research and experiment with various little projects and fun ways to incorporate new habits. I realized that our body is just like everything else and will become bored when it gets used to a routine. Once that happens, our success will waiver. That's when it's time to shake things up.

By mixing it up and trying different approaches, I was able to drop under 178 pounds about two and a half years ago and under 160 pounds seven or eight months after that. Various detours have caused my weight to fluctuate here and there, but I have stayed under 180 pounds for the past two years with few exceptions. I typically sit close to 170, but if I am under 180, I am happy. Without the 30–40 pounds of extra skin on my body, I know I would really weigh somewhere between 130 and 150 pounds, which is a greater achievement than I thought I would ever accomplish.

As I write this sentence, I weigh less than 160 pounds. In my book, that's a miracle!

CHAPTER 4

SHAME SPIRALS

The ultimate key to success is to simply get back on track, as often as it takes.

One of the biggest things that used to keep me from losing weight was getting stuck in a shame spiral. I would follow a food plan so well for a little while, and then I would fall off the wagon. I'd be so ashamed about falling off that I would beat myself up for failing and then eat more to numb those uncomfortable feelings so I could pretend I wasn't failing after all. This would go on and on until I had finally regained enough weight that I could no longer ignore what was happening.

It amazed me how hard it was to get back on track during a shame spiral. I just kept falling deeper and deeper into the spiral until I felt like I would never find my way out. Each unhealthy choice seemed to lead to another unhealthy choice. It seemed like a part of me would go wild because it was scared it would never get sugar again or something. That part of me would crave every unhealthy food imaginable. But nothing, no matter what I tried, would satisfy those cravings. Attempting to numb the feelings and shut up the inner critic—who was coming down hard on me for failing once again—wasn't working.

In time, the shame would grow so great that I would want to hide inside of it where the world couldn't see me and I didn't have to participate in activities with others. Giving in to the feeling, I would withdraw into the center of the shame and allow myself to feel even worse.

Once I became aware of these processes and cycles, they became so interesting to witness. I could begin using them to observe myself and attempt to understand my motivations and my triggers. This in turn has helped me learn to know myself more deeply and to become stronger as a result.

As I've "watched" myself get caught in shame spirals, I've learned just how vitally important it is to make a commitment to be kind and compassionate to myself in the midst of change, no matter what is happening. It's a brave decision to move forward in life and make changes in any self-improvement endeavor; and one way to honor that bravery is to know and accept that because we are human we will experience detours and struggle at times. We live in real life, and perfection does not exist in real life. What's important is progress and commitment fueled by self-acceptance and self-love. It's all OK. We are not in a race.

The ultimate key to success is to simply get back on track, as often as it takes. In the 48 months that have passed since I began my intense weight-loss project, I would say that 32 months have been full of healthy eating and good decisions and the other 16 I've taken detours. At least nine of those detours have been major ones. And at least three times I gained back between 15 and 25 pounds. Each time it took me 1–3 months to return to where I had started, but each time I also learned and gained confidence in my ability to get back on track before I had detoured too far off the path. And despite the detours, I have been maintaining my weight between 160 and 180 pounds. I believe that if we can achieve good decision-making 80 percent of the time when it comes to food, we are doing very well.

During each detour, I made a conscious decision to allow myself to step off the path and not give myself a hard time for failing again; I had developed enough trust that I knew I would get back on track again soon. I accepted that if I chose to eat foods that were high in sugar and low in nutrition, I would gain weight back. I also saw each occurrence as an opportunity and personal challenge to learn how to accept a setback, be compassionate, and redirect myself back to better decision-making regarding food choices. This was major progress compared to my early days when I expected perfection from myself and would view any deviations as complete failure and ruin, which would then lead to months and months of binging and treating my body unkindly.

In this new way of living, whenever I started making unhealthy food choices, I reflected and analyzed what was causing me to get off track. I would realize I was either super stressed from work, had some personal issue and was wanting to numb feelings, or had just become lazy because of holidays and special occasions.

One of the hardest times for me was mid-summer about three years ago when my son moved out and I became an empty nester. I was so proud of him for doing so well in his adult life, but I had not lived without him in 19 years. Then my sweet dog of 13 years died that December. During both of those occasions, my grief led me to seek solace in the old unhealthy pattern of eating junk food. The good news is that each time this happened, my comeback rate improved. I was able to reel myself in a bit and keep from going so far off the rails. I also proved to myself time and time again that I could keep going and stay committed to my health, my body, and myself no matter what.

When making decisions that we know are not good for us, it is so wise to be reflective and to attempt to listen to the battle going on inside of the mind. I knew that I wanted to be healthy, feel good, and make healthy food choices, yet I still allowed the detours to continue. What is going on when that happens?

It's an old familiar bad habit of mine called self-sabotage. When things have been going well for me and I have made more progress on my goals than I ever thought possible, I often find myself battling with another side of the inner critic that says, "Who do you think you are to make such progress?" The question brings to life the skeletons of not feeling good enough or worthy of my dreams.

For instance, now that I am finally putting pen to paper and investing time and energy into writing this book, the inner saboteur is raising her loud, fear-filled voice. Of course, I would try to self-sabotage the success of the very thing about which I am writing! It is such an old story, and I deserve so much better than I have allowed myself to experience. Now that I am aware of all of this, I will make an empowered choice to keep moving forward. Authoring this book is a dream come true for me, no matter what the outcome.

CHAPTER 5

A REALISTIC PLAN

If you fail to plan, you are planning to fail!
—Benjamin Franklin

Constructing a realistic plan is a crucial part of the journey to better health. As I share my own steps for a solid plan to improved health, I suggest you listen for whatever resonates with you and then adopt whatever actually works for you—whether it's something I share in these pages or something you've discovered elsewhere.

In my early attempts to improve my health, I failed more often than I succeeded. Over the years, however, I have developed a much more realistic and balanced approach. Now I first determine my ultimate goal, being honest with myself about what I can actually do and who I really am. Then I select several small goals that I can meet early on. After deciding what my commitment and responsibility will be, I put my plan in writing and set out to begin implementing it the best way I know how, checking in with others for support and re-evaluation as needed.

I do all this with the knowledge and wisdom that things could change and that I must remain flexible. I also believe that

I will be led by the wisdom of a power greater than myself that knows my greater good better than I do.

Determine your ultimate goal

To determine what your ultimate goal is, begin by asking yourself some of the following important questions:

- What do you want to achieve or experience? Why do you want this?
- What do you think you have to do to reach this goal?
- What kind of commitment would you need to make?
- Is that realistic for you in your life right now? (If the answer to this is no, then rethink your goal and choose a smaller, more achievable goal for yourself.)
- What would be some smaller goals you could achieve along the way and celebrate?
- What are you 100 percent willing to do to achieve your goals?
- What are you afraid will get in the way?
- What strategies can you use to get back on track if your fears come true?
- What methods or actions do you want to take to achieve each goal?
- Have you done research related to these goals?
- When would you like to begin this process?

Be honest and realistic

During this process, it's important to be honest with yourself about what will fit into your lifestyle. Realistically, what are all the factors in your life to consider when constructing a plan for your goals?

For instance, when I began this adventure four years ago, my son was 18 years old and our work schedules did not allow a daily meal together. Since he took care of his own dietary needs and I was separated from my partner at the time, I had a great deal of freedom to choose my approach to losing weight. I knew I could commit to going big for the first few months.

For me, going big meant I would be eliminating almost all sugar other than a few berries. I stuck with that strict plan for over 60 days and lost 44 pounds. This would not be a realistic goal for most people, or even myself again, to lose that much weight that quickly. But at 278 pounds, I had hit a low point in my life. Depleted, drained, and worn out from caring for everyone else, I realized I needed to do something big for myself and invest in me. I needed to prove to myself that I could accomplish something major and that I was still a powerful and strong woman. I also wanted to achieve enough weight loss to keep me motivated, to make me not want to thwart the great progress I had made.

During that same period of time, one of my best friends was also trying to lose weight and get healthier, but her life was much different from mine. With three young kids and a husband, she was responsible for preparing several meals a day for five people and was not motivated to cook separate meals for herself. Nor was she interested in completely changing the way her family ate just to accommodate her desire to lose weight fast. She also loved bread and was not willing to give it up. So for her, Weight Watchers seemed to be the best fit. She knew and accepted from the start that her weight-loss journey would be slow and steady, and it totally worked for her!

Be uniquely you

Being honest with yourself includes learning to know what makes you unique. As you set your goals, strive to become your authentic self rather than setting goals just to conform to what society and other people say you ought to be like. Be ok being uniquely you.

One of my greatest lessons learned is to set realistic goals based on what I want for myself. I do not need to mold to society's standards, and neither do you! We do not need cookie-cutter templates of each other walking around. And we do not have to believe the myths we have been told either. We do not have to be thin to be healthy, and externals will only get people so far in life. We want to reach for self-acceptance and self-love. We want to learn to be comfortable in our own skin and how to become our own best friend and advocate. Developing that relationship, reliance, and trust in ourselves is truly the most important part of this journey.

Part of my uniqueness means accepting that the mirror is not going to accurately reflect to me all the hard work I have put in, because I now have extra skin hanging on my body that will most likely need to be surgically removed. I must choose to love and accept myself anyway and be proud of the 300-plus pounds I have lost. I love me, and I am okay. It's only because of society that the extra skin is considered a flaw, and one day if I am meant to have it removed I will. Otherwise, I am just thrilled that I am healthier, my body feels much better, and I can move around more freely. I am grateful for the journey I have been on and that I finally feel worthy to keep this weight off and leave obesity behind me.

Select three goals

After you've spent some time with the above questions, identify one goal that is achievable for you the first week, one goal that is achievable the first month, and a more long-term goal of three or six months. Then, make your commitment and pick the day you will begin. This will allow you to feel some success as soon as possible.

Put it in writing

I highly recommend putting your plans in writing. I have found it extremely helpful to write all my plans and results down in a notebook or journal. It makes them more tangible and helps me stay accountable to the process. Plus, I have loved looking back at all the progress I've made.

Get the support and assistance you need

Ensure that you have supportive people in your life that you can talk to and seek advice and wisdom from when needed. This may include professionals, friends, or co-workers that you trust and know you can count on. Be sure to set good boundaries for yourself, and do not discuss your journey and progress with any person who will be negative or discouraging. If you need professional help and support, do not be afraid to get that for yourself. There is nothing more important than your investment in you.

* * *

We must set ourselves up for success. I don't know about you, but I have made so many unrealistic goals and plans in my life. I have failed repeatedly and then felt horrible and ashamed of myself, which then led me to make unhealthy food choices for comfort. Through my repeated failures, I have learned the importance of setting specific, achievable goals that can fit into my current life situation.

It is so awesome to look out for myself and choose a path where success is totally achievable!

CHAPTER 6

DISCIPLINE AND FLEXIBILITY

Find what works for you.

Once you have created a realistic plan for your goals, it's time to apply commitment and discipline to accomplish those goals. As you proceed, however, it's important to accept that your plan will likely change along the way. Flexibility is key. And for me, spontaneity, joy, and just plain having fun are equally as important as having a solid plan.

Be disciplined

At some point a solid plan needs to be put in place that can be followed consistently. But what does being consistent mean? How long does it take to break a bad habit and start a new one? There are various theories on this. Some people say 21 days and some people say 40 days. In my experience, it took more than a month of repetition for my brain and body to get on board with something new. Find what works for you.

During the initial couple years of the global COVID-19 pandemic, I personally found sticking with my health plan to be somewhat of a roller coaster ride. The first year I battled with craving sugar and unhealthy carbs and sought comfort in my old habits. Some days I gave in to those cravings, but no matter what I consistently returned to my health plan and continued to keep my weight under 180 pounds. I was able to remain compassionate, nonjudgmental, honest, and realistic with myself, which I believe has been a critical part of my long-term success in weight loss.

Be flexible

As you meet goals and experiment with different approaches, you may want to shift your plan around a bit. And there may be periods when you have to take things just one day at a time. In times of great stress, for instance, when there are family members or work situations that need your time and attention, you will need to adjust your expectations of yourself and be extra compassionate and patient.

In my own life, I've made a number of significant shifts. The year I had gastric bypass surgery, my plan was to listen to as much of the doctors' guidance as I could and allow the newly created pouch to work its magic. Eleven years later, my new plan was to follow a strict diet for 6–12 weeks and track everything I ate daily, as well as to weigh myself every single day. In addition, I went to the doctor once a week and weighed in for accountability and support. The following two years my plan was to experiment with different fasting methods to see which ones felt best to my body.

I continue to be flexible and adjust my plans as needed.

Be flexibly disciplined

We live our richest life when we combine discipline with flexibility in a way that best suits our individual needs. Here are two examples of how I have integrated both in my own life.

Celebrate and return to plan

One of the biggest challenges to staying on plan can be our culture's practice of celebrating many occasions with food. A realistic approach acknowledges this and recognizes that there will be times of indulgence and eating unhealthy food. Once our body is healthier, it can handle such occasions and bounce back quickly as long as we get right back on track with our health plan. How liberating and freeing to know this! So celebrate and then return to plan!

Weigh yourself, but let go of the scales

Have you ever been obsessed with the number on your bathroom scales? Has that number taken charge of too much of your life? For me, the answer is a big yes. Too often I have stepped on the scales, seen that I haven't lost weight, and immediately heard my harsh inner critic start attacking me. I would listen to the voice, start judging myself, and feel terrible about who I was. At some point, I realized I was not willing to be captive to that voice anymore and decided that letting go of the number on the scales would be giving myself a huge gift of kindness.

I still weigh myself but do so now with more realistic expectations. For starters, adults can easily fluctuate 4–6 pounds in water weight. Because of this, I make sure to weigh in only once a week and at the same time in the morning after I wake up. I also know that because of the extra skin on my body, it is unrealistic to for me expect to match what the health charts say I should weigh. I also do not step on the scales when I am menstruating, because I always weigh more during that time.[9]

****

As you pursue your goals, be willing to get to know yourself and understand your own needs so that you can give yourself genuine self-acceptance, self-love, and self-compassion. And in the process of improving yourself, be willing to be patient and nonjudgmental with yourself. Improving your life is a huge undertaking, and you deserve to be proud of yourself for even attempting to make changes.

In the end, what matters is how we feel, right? Does it really matter what number shows up on the scales or whether we stuck to our plan 100 percent if we feel good and are happy with our progress?

---

[9] If you are working out and building muscle, be aware that muscle can add weight, at least in the short-term.

CHAPTER 7

10 KEYS TO SUCCESS

You will be with yourself for the rest of your life, so any effort toward enjoying your life more is worth it!

This chapter is a cheat sheet for those of you who like to have everything summarized in one tidy little area. Here are 10 of the key practices that have led the way to achieving my own personal goals and that can help you do the same.

Ten Keys to Success

1. **Change your thoughts.** Pay attention to what you are thinking and saying to yourself in your mind. Work on saying new things to yourself that reflect what you want to experience.

2. **Identify limiting beliefs and reasons for why you are where you are.** Take the time to reflect upon your life and recall the messages you have received throughout

the years. Consider reading some books about this if you need extra support. It is so valuable to understand how you developed your limiting beliefs and life issues so that you can use that knowledge to resolve them.

3. **Encourage and accept yourself along the way.** Be mindful and pay attention to when you go into self-sabotage mode or let the inner critic take you on a shame spiral. Become your own loving and supportive advocate. Talk to yourself the way you would talk to someone you love and respect. If you can't be kind to yourself, please seek out professional assistance.

4. **Get the help and support you need.** Make sure to include self-care in your routine. If you need therapy, medical opinions, or a support group, seek it out! Reading about other success stories and information relevant to weight loss was so helpful for me. Having supportive people to discuss my progress with online was also very encouraging and helped me keep going. Set good boundaries for yourself and do not discuss your weight-loss journey with anyone who will be discouraging and negative. You only need people who will cheer you on and offer positive and uplifting support.

5. **Celebrate your achievements along the way.** Find non-food related rewards to give yourself when you meet goals and milestones.

6. **Monitor your progress.** Keeping track of my weekly weigh-ins and journaling about my feelings and progress has been a huge part of my continued success.

7. **Keep going.** When you fall, get right back up and begin again.

8. **Document your lessons learned, and apply continued knowledge along the way.** Re-reading what has worked for you and reflecting on how you've changed will fuel your motivation to keep going and see what more you can accomplish. It amazes me and the people in my life how much I have changed for the better throughout the years and how evident this change is from my journal entries and documented lessons learned.

9. **Be willing to implement variety and try new approaches.** Research different methods and avenues of success and be willing to try them to see if they may work for you. This makes the experience of self-improvement so much more fun! If I had tried only one strategy to lose weight or to accomplish any other goal in my life, I would not have had long-term success.

10. **Never give up on yourself.** When things are more challenging, take it one day at a time or one hour at a time. You will be with yourself for the rest of your life, so any effort toward enjoying your life more is worth it!

It's a multi-layered journey

Losing weight, especially when it is a large amount of weight, is a multi-layered physical, mental, and emotional journey.

- **The physical level** will consist of taking the action steps that must be done to lose weight—in other words, participating in the actual process of losing the weight.

- **The mental level** will include creating realistic goals, coming up with a plan to meet those goals, disciplining yourself to stick with your plan, and uncovering psychological blocks and issues. This will also involve taking the time to talk kindly to yourself and committing to treat yourself well, especially when you encounter challenges and setbacks.

- **The emotional level** will include allowing old wounds and traumas to come up as you learn how to feel your feelings instead of stuffing them down with food. It will also consist of exploring new ways to find comfort and soothing that are non-food related.

- **The spiritual level** will consist of developing a deeper relationship with your true self and becoming your authentic self. This will include learning how to become your own best friend and ally.

You are worth it!

The results of this undertaking will be so rewarding and nothing less than miraculous if you stay committed to reaching your goals. It does not matter how long it takes; if you keep coming back to yourself, you will achieve self-improvement and be a much happier person than you were when you started the journey. Learning to give yourself the gift of self-acceptance is so worth the effort. And *you* are worth the effort!

CHAPTER 8

ADDITIONAL MIRACLES FROM INNER WORK

Self-acceptance is the gift of a lifetime.

Me celebrating the miracles of my life

My path to self-acceptance and self-love has given me so much more than weight loss. It has also blessed me with many additional miracles and rewards that have flowed out of the gift of this way of life. I'll share some of those miracles and rewards here.

An Incredibly Rewarding Career

I have always wanted to have a solid career. In fact, I had hoped my career would be one of my greatest successes in life as an adult. So dropping out of college at age 18 and then going back four years later when I weighed over 400 pounds was not an easy decision. Although I felt very guided to make those decisions so I could create a better life for my son, the odds of being accepted to college the second time around were not in my favor because I had applied just three weeks before classes were scheduled to begin. I needed financial aid, and the advisors doubted it would come through in time. Using all the inner healing skills I had learned up to that point, I affirmed that I would be approved for financial aid and believed it would happen.

And it did. Exactly as I had affirmed. I even landed my first job in cybersecurity the last semester of college through a recommendation from my IT professor. I began working at that job in April, one month before I graduated with my associates degree. Over the next two years, I doubled the salary I was making in customer service. Using the skills I had learned to change my thinking and internal beliefs, I then built and was blessed with an incredible career in the IT field. I continued to believe and affirm I was worthy and wrote down all that I wanted to experience and create in my life.

Four years into my IT work, management personnel informed me that if I stayed on my current team, I would not be given the team lead role that I wanted and had earned. I chose to believe differently. Within a year, a new boss came on board and promoted me to team lead. For a year, I got to perform in the role of Information Assurance Trainer, which gave me the privilege of developing and creating a training department as well as traveling to many different places to train people on software. I also had the opportunity to teach people how to implement risk management processes and procedures and became quite efficient at continual process improvement.

It's now been 17 years since my first IT job, and I have had the most incredible experiences in my career. I'm grateful for the amazing achievement of creating and building an absolute dream team experience as well as seeing my leadership skills develop a flourishing work environment and a happy team that resulted in a prestigious award. It is so gratifying to know that others beyond our team experienced the ripple effects of our creative work together.

My award-winning team accepting the Team of the Quarter award.

Celebrating with my team after winning the award.

Posing with my dream team at a team luncheon.

The Perfect House for My Little Family

After my gastric bypass surgery, I was on a roll of manifesting positive things in my life. I decided I wanted to find a more permanent location to live, where I could buy a house that my son and I could settle into. After much thought and writing down affirmations, I was guided to a beautiful place that I could rent to own. At exactly the right time, two years after my surgery, I was awarded a raise that made it possible for me to pay the $400 increase in payment.

When the owners went to officially sell the house to me, however, it didn't appraise for what they wanted, and my hopes of owning the home were dashed. I was so confused that the deal didn't work out, because I was certain the house was meant to be ours. Nevertheless, I surrendered the outcome. A year later, the owners had to do a short sale, and I bought the house for $65,000 less than the original asking price. That was so awesome!

Parenting: Breaking Ancestral Patterns

It is accurate to say that I did not have any good models for the most effective way to be a parent. Knowing this, I put even more effort into being an effective and loving mother than I did into my weight-loss efforts. As a parent, I was responsible for the well-being of another person, and I treated that responsibility as a sacred duty. I made sure to read multiple books on parenting, and I researched for countless hours because I did not want my son to feel the way I had felt growing up. I was determined to help teach him to love and accept himself from the start. I wanted him to feel unconditionally loved, and I am beyond proud to say that I succeeded at that task. I did plenty of learning and readjusting along the way, but the whole experience was deeply healing.

It is equally miraculous that the experience of parenting and wonderful relationship with my son successfully broke many of the previous ancestral patterns in my family line. Nick and I created a whole new paradigm together. That miracle is even more significant than my achievement of losing weight.

Going out for an evening of music with my son

Enjoying a hike together.

Beautiful and true friendships

I believe friendship is a great art. Sadly, I notice many people these days seem like they have not learned this skill and appear unhappy in their friend relationships. I'm fortunate that I began at a very young age to focus on being a wonderful friend to others. As I grew older, I also grew in my willingness to set boundaries and let go of people who were not good for me. Because of this, I am blessed with multiple friendships, some of them going back all the way to age six—more than three decades. It is truly a blessing to share in the joy of high-quality friendships filled with mutual love, appreciation, and depth.

Loving romantic relationship

After many trials and tribulations over the years with romantic partners, I was caught off guard about 10 years ago when my best friend from age 15 asked me to go out with him. We have had our ups and downs and learned so much together over the years, but our love story is now over a decade old, and no matter what the future holds, we are each so grateful for the experience of true love and connection. Both of us are sensitive souls with traumatic childhoods, and we have been able to provide each other with a safe place to be honored, loved, and appreciated. We have never lost the passion and bond from when we first started dating.

Training with my favorite author

About seven years ago I was able to somehow manifest the abundance needed to attend five different trainings with my favorite author over the course of two years. I learned so much from those experiences, and I will forever be grateful for them.

Posing with my teacher, Sonia Choquette.

Reuniting with my dad's family after 29 years

When my grandmother died 20 years ago, I lost contact with my dad's family because of family drama with the will. Surprisingly, about two years ago I received a letter that said I may be eligible for a small inheritance from my grandmother's estate. This led to phone calls with my dad's brother and niece as well as my two half-brothers. Not long after that, I got to see my uncle and cousin, and we have been in contact ever since. I also received a small inheritance and was able to pay off some of my debt last year. That was such a huge miracle!

Reunited after 30 years.

Reiki for my grandparents

About 13 years ago my grandmother got sick, and the following year my grandfather was diagnosed with lung cancer. Neither of them had previously believed in any sort of alternative healing, and they thought my interest and training in Reiki was silly. At an oncologist appointment for my grandfather, however, my grandparents saw a poster about Reiki, which opened their minds to its healing potential. I had the honor of giving them healing treatments for two to three years before my grandmother died. My grandfather, who died a couple years later, lived two to three years longer than his doctors anticipated. I believe Reiki contributed to that miracle.

***

While weight loss has been one of the most significant and complex goals and achievements of my life so far, it is equally important to mention these other incredible experiences that have evolved out of my commitment to do inner healing work.[10] Because the beauty of such work is that it doesn't stop with weight loss.

Enjoying my ability to move more.

---

[10] I intend to write more about some of these experiences in the future and to offer support and encouragement to others for multiple aspects of life.

Feeling free and happy FINALLY.

CHAPTER 9

A WORD OF ENCOURAGEMENT

Everything we do for our own healing benefits everyone else in our life.

I hope I have made three things crystal clear in these pages—that we do not have to suffer anymore; that every person has the ability to choose to do the inner work necessary to reclaim their personal power; and that anyone who makes a commitment to invest in themselves and their own healing will become the recipient of many gifts, blessings, and miracles.

What it takes is a brave choice to learn how to love, embrace, and accept ourselves with all our human flaws. We must decide to love ourselves enough to get the help we truly need to move forward once and for all, to stop beating ourselves up and sabotaging our self-improvement efforts. For anyone who takes the time to dig into exploring their inner world, monumental opportunities are available for deep healing from all forms of trauma and suffering. Many books, classes, and health professionals are available to assist with this journey.

We can decide how we want to live and feel so that we can create a new beginning for ourselves. We can choose to review our life so that we can make positive changes to rewire our thinking and reprogram our brain to operate in a way that will bring us desired outcomes. We can choose to break out of the shackles of victimhood and become self-empowered. We can set boundaries, make goals, construct plans, and have fun in our efforts to create new experiences in our life. It only takes one self-accepting, self-loving choice at a time, one day at a time.

In the process, we will learn that our most difficult struggles are usually just symptoms masking deeper issues. Then we can learn from our experiences and allow the painful times to make us stronger, more empathic, and more compassionate with ourselves and others. And as we get to know ourselves and examine our lives and upbringings, we can break unhealthy patterns of thought and action that have been passed down from generation to generation.

Such a process will take different amounts of time depending on the severity of the situation and depth of the wounding. But some basic steps can help anyone: choosing to focus on what we love in our life, what we are grateful for, what we appreciate, and what makes us happy; choosing to do more of what brings us joy; and practicing this again and again. As we do this, it will become easier and easier to create the life circumstances and experiences we want. All it takes is practice, time, and a commitment to keep moving forward no matter how many times we start over.

Along the way, we do not need to compare ourselves and our progress to anyone else. When our mind wanders into negative territory and we catch ourselves in lower feeling states, we can simply acknowledge the feelings, feel them, explore them, reframe them, and choose a new thought or thought pattern.

Given our Western society's tendency to cause us to feel unworthy and look outside ourselves for relief, it is more important than ever to choose to look within and do the inner work necessary to move forward in creating a better life for ourselves, our loved ones, and future generations. We have been suffering and beating ourselves up long enough. It's time to attempt a new approach to living life. Everything we do for our own healing benefits everyone else in our life. I think we could all use more happiness, joy, positivity, love, and inspiration right now. How about you?

I am so grateful I found a way to get past my own wounds and sought out the help and assistance I needed over the years to move forward in my life. I only wish I had learned how to approach self-improvement efforts with self-acceptance, self-compassion, and self-love at a younger age. We don't have enough models for this yet, but I believe there will many more examples and role models in the coming years.

I hope my story has inspired you to gift yourself with self-acceptance and commitment to doing your own inner work so you can experience all the well-deserved miracles that will result from that one empowering decision. It's a gift that will truly keep on giving.

ABOUT THE AUTHOR

Melanie Weaver's deeply caring heart and inquisitive mind have led her on a unique path of simultaneously studying business and alternative healing, resulting in both a traditional business degree and non-traditional Reiki Master certificate in 2005. She has taken courses in various leadership, management, and training techniques in her now 17-year cybersecurity career, as well as studied multiple healing and intuitive modalities throughout her 41 years on the planet. Her interests are varied, but at the heart of all she does is a deep desire to inspire, help, and mentor others—no matter their circumstances—in navigating the depths of inner work to overcome past wounding and achieve more peace, self-confidence, and personal empowerment.

Melanie has been climbing metaphorical mountains her whole life and has found peace and liberation from many obstacles along the way. She has overcome a lifelong battle with obesity that peaked at 480 pounds as a young adult; transcended childhood trauma and abuse; and traversed the path of single parenting beginning at age 18. Her experiences provide a living example of navigating and persevering through the ups and downs of life to reach rewarding mountaintop victories.

Melanie's personal healing journey and professional experience in leadership and mentoring have brought her to a place in life where her deep desire is to inspire and empower others to overcome the obstacles on their own paths so they can experience the joy of living.

More information about Melanie and her story can be found at http://www.melanieweaver.online/about.html.

A note from the author

To stay connected with me, visit my website at http://www.melanieweaver.online/, and sign up to be on my mailing list. You can also contact me at melaniemweaver40@gmail.com.

Stay tuned for topics of special interest that I'd love to develop resources for in addition to weight loss: healthy eating, mentorship, job & career growth, leadership, process improvement, single parenting, parenting in general, spirituality & healing, and friendship.

Let me know what kind of other information and support you would like. I would love to hear from you!

CPSIA information can be obtained
at www.ICGtesting.com
Printed in the USA
BVHW071240020822
643617BV00006B/171

9 798986 135403